Biff and Chip liked the new house.
They helped Mum and Dad.

Mum put wallpaper on the wall.
Chip helped her.

Dad painted a door. Biff helped him.

Biff was in her room. Dad
looked at the wallpaper.

Biff wanted new wallpaper.

They went to the wallpaper
shop.

Biff looked at the wallpaper.
She liked this wallpaper.

Mum and Dad pulled the
wallpaper off.

Biff and Chip helped.
"What a job!" said Chip.

Biff found a door.

The door was stuck.

Mum opened the door. She found
a room.

Everyone looked inside.

Mum went into the secret room.
She found a little house.

"It looks like our house,"
said Mum.

Biff opened the little house.
Everyone looked inside.

"It looks like our house inside,"
said Biff.

Kipper found a little dog.
"Look at this little dog,"
said Kipper.

"It looks like our dog. It looks like Floppy."

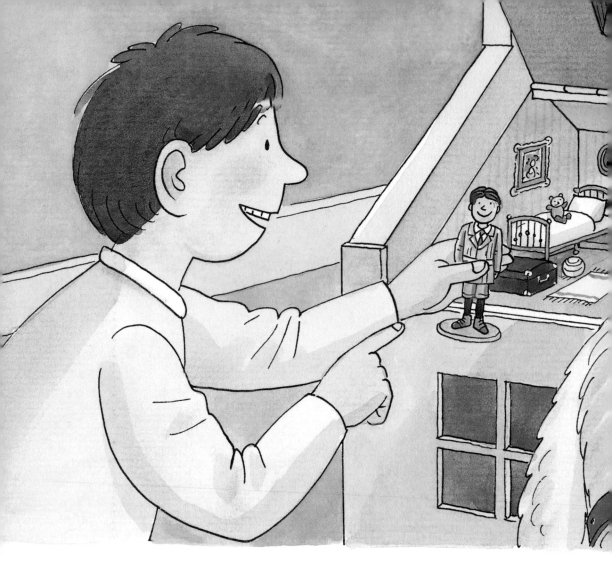

Chip found three little children.

"Look at the children," said Chip.
"They look like us."

Biff liked her bedroom. She
liked the secret room too.

Dad painted the secret room.
Biff put things inside.

Biff was in bed. She was fast
asleep. She dreamed about the
little children.

24